3, 2
Blastoff!

Published by
Andrea Hartmann
Cedar Rapids, Iowa
ISBN# 978-0-9837999-0-0

Illustrated by **Kylee Pastore**

For more information about this book, please contact us:
contact@hartmannfamily.us

Dedicated to my firstborn,
Promise Michael
Hartmann.

He was born prematurely
weighing 3 lbs 15.1 oz.

I love you, son.
You truly
are a blessing
from God.

This book is my own fun way of explaining to young children the events surrounding the premature birth of Promise Michael.

My prayer is that this book will bring comfort to families who have or know of an infant in the NICU.

My Story

Hi, my name is Promise Michael...

When I was born,
I lived in a spaceship.

I even got to wear a special space helmet!

To prepare for my big flight, I had to pass many tests.

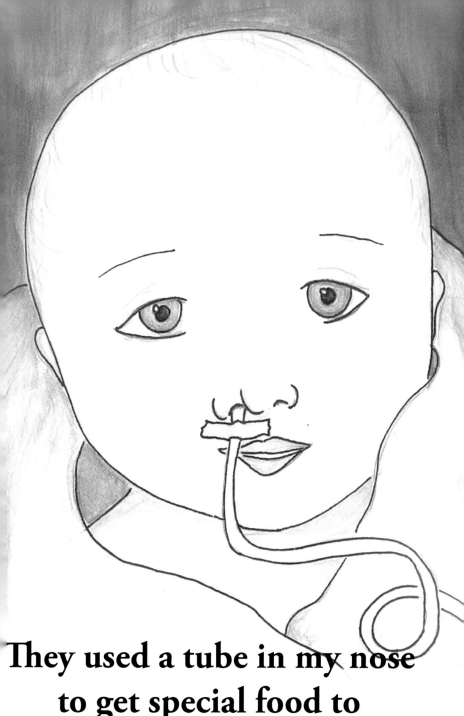

They used a tube in my nose
to get special food to
my belly.

My parents proudly stayed to help me with my training.

Each day I got closer to the day of my big flight.

BLASTOFF!!!

The Real Story

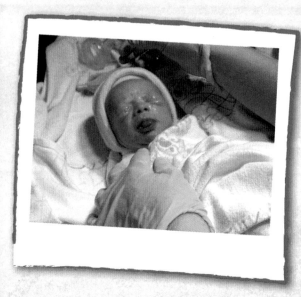

Promise Michael was born on August 8th, 2006 at Fairbanks Memorial Hospital in Fairbanks, Alaska.

He weighed
3 pounds
15.1 ounces.

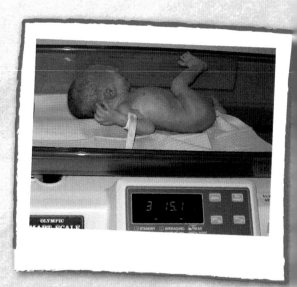

Thankfully, Promise Michael only had to stay under the oxy-hood for his first day.

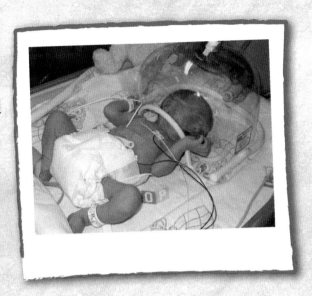

He may have been under weight, but his lungs were NOT under developed.

His Dad says he was one of the loudest in the NICU.

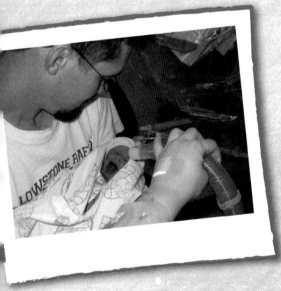

The "Spaceship"

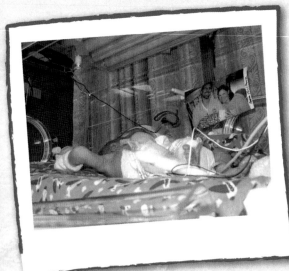

We decorated his incubator with airplane sheets, a teddy bear, a picture of us, and hooked up a MP3 player to play classical hymns 24/7!

Our sweet boy was covered in wires, "leads", sensors and a feeding tube...

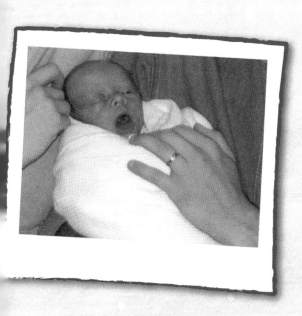

but not
for long!!!

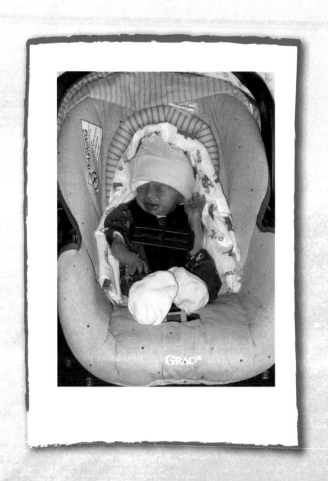

After three long weeks and
weighing just over four pounds,
Promise Michael was allowed to
come home with us.

Having a child in the
NICU can be very hard,
and we hope that this book will
bring you some comfort.

We also hope that this book
will help children who may have
a new born sibling in the NICU
better understand what
is going on.

Blessings,
The Hartmann Family

contact@hartmannfamily.us